In **Bits and Pieces I,** you concentrated on understanding what fractions, decimals, and percents mean. In this unit, you will investigate situations—like those described on the opposite page—in which you need to add, subtract, multiply, or divide fractions and decimals. You will need to think about which operation makes sense in each situation.

Knowing strategies for computing with all kinds of numbers is very important. If you take part in developing these strategies, they will make more sense to you, and you will be able to apply them to other situations. You may already know some shortcuts for computing with fractions and decimals. You can get the most out of this unit by thinking about why those shortcuts—and the new strategies you develop with your class—make sense. Remember, it is not enough to get an answer to a problem. The real power is in being able to talk about your ideas and strategies.

W0006153

Mathematical Highlights

In *Bits and Pieces II*, you will learn about operations with fractions, decimals, and percents.

- Computing discounts, taxes, and tips shows you that understanding operations with percents is helpful in situations involving money.

- Working with the results of surveys gives you practice computing percents of totals that are greater than or less than 100.

- Creating circle graphs lets you represent data that fall into nonoverlapping categories.

- Playing the Getting Close game sharpens your skills at estimating sums of fractions and decimals.

- As you investigate transactions in which land is bought and sold, you develop strategies for adding and subtracting fractions.

- Adding and subtracting fractions helps you make sense of the havoc caused by the infamous Pizza Pirate.

- What you know about sums and differences helps you write algorithms—or organized plans—for adding and subtracting fractions.

- Drawing diagrams to model portions of pans of brownies leads you to discover a pattern for multiplying fractions.

- What you know about products helps you write an *algorithm* for multiplying fractions.

- Playing a game in which you purchase school supplies gives you practice estimating sums and differences of decimal numbers.

- Multiplying related sets of numbers illustrates how the number of decimal places in the factors relates to the number of decimal places in the product.

- Finding numbers with a given product helps you develop a deeper understanding of multiplication.

Using Percents

In *Bits and Pieces I,* you discovered that percents are useful for reporting the results of surveys. Percents are also helpful in situations involving money. Discounts, taxes, and tips are all described with percents. Understanding what these percents mean and how they are used can make you a smarter consumer.

1.1 Taxing Tapes

Remember that a percent is a special way of representing a fraction with a denominator of 100. You can think of percent as meaning "out of 100."

Let's begin by looking at sales tax. A sales tax of 6% means that for every dollar an item costs, a person needs to pay an additional six hundredths of a dollar, or $0.06:

$1.00 + (6% of $1.00) = $1.00 + $0.06 = $1.06

Or, since $1.00 is 100 pennies:

100 pennies + (6% of 100 pennies) = 100 pennies + 6 pennies = 106 pennies = $1.06

Problem 1.1

Jill wants to buy a cassette tape that is priced at $7.50. The sales tax is 6%. What will be the total cost of the tape? Try to find more than one way to solve this problem. Be prepared to explain the different methods you find.

■ Problem 1.1 Follow-Up

Developing shortcuts can help make estimating tax easier. To find a shortcut, you can begin by examining a way to mark hundredths grids to show percents. The grids below show what an item would cost if the price were $1.00 and the tax were 6%.

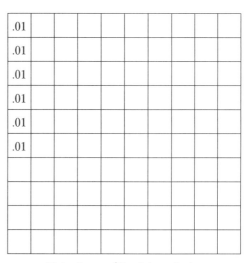

.01	.01	.01	.01	.01	.01	.01	.01	.01	.01
.01	.01	.01	.01	.01	.01	.01	.01	.01	.01
.01	.01	.01	.01	.01	.01	.01	.01	.01	.01
.01	.01	.01	.01	.01	.01	.01	.01	.01	.01
.01	.01	.01	.01	.01	.01	.01	.01	.01	.01
.01	.01	.01	.01	.01	.01	.01	.01	.01	.01
.01	.01	.01	.01	.01	.01	.01	.01	.01	.01
.01	.01	.01	.01	.01	.01	.01	.01	.01	.01
.01	.01	.01	.01	.01	.01	.01	.01	.01	.01
.01	.01	.01	.01	.01	.01	.01	.01	.01	.01

This shows 100% of the whole, which is $1.00.

This shows 6% of the whole, which is $0.06.

You would pay $1.06 for the item.

1. Use what you have discovered about percents to help you solve these problems. Explain your reasoning.
   a. What is the total price for a magazine that costs $2.00 plus 6% tax?
   b. What is the total price for a book on dogs that costs $5.00 plus 6% tax?
   c. What is the total price for a comic book that costs $0.50 plus 6% tax?

2. Solve each problem. When you finish, describe any patterns you observe.
   a. What is the total price for a balloon that costs $1.00 plus 5% tax?
   b. What is the total price for a balloon that costs $1.00 plus 6% tax?
   c. What is the total price for a balloon that costs $1.00 plus 7% tax?
   d. What is the total price for a balloon that costs $1.00 plus 8% tax?
3. Use what you learned in questions 1 and 2 to help you answer these questions. Explain your reasoning.
   a. What is the total price of a pack of tennis balls that costs $5.00 plus 3% tax?
   b. What is the total price of a calculator that costs $19.50 plus 8% tax?
4. Kiah bought a portable cassette player. She does not remember the price, but she does know that the 6% sales tax was $4.80. What was the price of the portable cassette player? Explain your reasoning.
5. Frank bought a new video game. The 5% sales tax was $0.75. What was the price of the game? Explain your reasoning.

1.2 Computing Tips

At most restaurants, customers pay their server a tip for providing good service. A typical tip is 15% to 20% of the cost of the meal. Some people calculate the tip based on the cost of the meal *before* the tax is added, and others use the cost of the meal *after* the tax is added.

You have just finished lunch at Larry's Lunch Place. The food was delicious, and the service was excellent! The bill has just arrived.

Problem 1.2

Have each member of your group use the menu your teacher provides to make up a lunch order. Write all the items ordered by your group on the order check. Total the bill, and add your local sales tax.

A. What is your total bill for food and tax?

B. How much will you leave for the tip? (The tip must be between 15% and 20%.)

C. The members of your group decide to share the cost of the meal equally. About how much would each person need to contribute to pay the bill as well as the tip?

Try to find more than one way to solve parts A and B. Be prepared to explain the different methods you used.

■ Problem 1.2 Follow-Up

1. Many people use benchmarks for determining tips. Jim explains his strategy for finding a tip: "I always figure out 10% of the bill, and then I use this information to calculate a 15% or 20% tip."

   a. Find 10% and 5% of $20.00. Explain how the two percents are related.

   b. Find 10% and 20% of $24.50. Explain how the two percents are related.

   c. Find 10% of $17.35. Use this to find 15% and 20% of $17.35. Explain your reasoning.

2. The sales tax in Kadisha's state is 5%. Kadisha says she computes a 15% tip by multiplying the tax shown on her bill by 3. For the bill shown here, Kadisha's tip would be $0.38 × 3 = $1.14.

Garden Cafe	
ITEM	AMOUNT
Food	$7.55
5% Tax	.38
TOTAL	$7.93

   a. Why does Kadisha's method work?

   b. Use a similar method to compute a 20% tip on Kadisha's bill. Explain your answer.

   c. Does Kadisha's method give 15% of the *entire bill* (including tax) or 15% of the cost *before* tax is added? Explain your thinking.

3. When people leave a 15% or 20% tip, they often round up to the nearest multiple of 5 or 10 cents. For example, in question 2, Kadisha might leave a tip of $1.15 rather than $1.14.

   a. If Kadisha always rounds up, what would she likely leave for a 20% tip on her bill?

   b. Omar always leaves a 20% tip based on the meal price before tax is added. Find a meal price for which Omar would leave a tip of $1.00 after rounding up to the nearest multiple of 5 or 10 cents.

   c. Marlene always leaves a 15% tip based on the meal price before tax is added. Find a meal price for which Marlene would leave a tip of $4.50 after rounding up to the nearest multiple of 5 or 10 cents.

   d. Customers left Jerome $2.50 as a tip for service. The tip was 20% of the bill for their food. How much was the bill?

1.3 **Finding Bargains**

At Loud Sounds Music Warehouse, CDs are regularly priced at $9.95 and tapes are regularly priced at $6.95. Every day this month, the store is offering a 10% discount on all CDs and tapes.

Problem 1.3

Joshua and Jeremy go to Loud Sounds to buy a tape and a CD. They do not have much money, so they have pooled their funds. When they get to the store, they find that there is another discount plan available just for that day—if they buy three or more items, they can save 20% (instead of 10%) on each item.

A. If they buy a CD and a tape, how much money will they spend after the store adds a 6% sales tax on the discounted prices?

B. Jeremy says he thinks they can buy three tapes for less money than the cost of a tape and a CD. Is he correct? Explain your reasoning.

Try to find more than one way to solve these problems. Be prepared to explain the different methods you discover.

■ Problem 1.3 Follow-Up

1. Mr. Knapp wants to take advantage of the day's special to fill out his CD collection. There are 15 CDs he wants to buy.
   a. What is the total amount of the discount he will receive?
   b. What will the 15 CDs cost after a 6% sales tax has been added?

2. Look back at question 1.

   a. If the discount were only 1%, what total discount amount would Mr. Knapp receive on the 15 CDs?

   b. What is the relationship between 1% of the cost of 15 CDs and 20% of the cost of 15 CDs?

   c. If the discount were 10%, what total discount amount would Mr. Knapp receive for the 15 CDs?

   d. How is a 10% discount related to a 20% discount?

   e. How is a 10% discount related to a 1% discount?

   f. How could you use what you know about a 10% discount on the cost of the 15 CDs to find a 15% discount on the cost of the CDs?

   g. How could you use what you found out above to find a 16% discount on the cost of the 15 CDs? Can you find another way to compute 16% of the cost of the CDs? Explain your methods and how they are related.

3. You have been finding percents of numbers to compute taxes and tips. Explain how you can find *any* percent of a given number.

1.4 Spending Money

Do you ever keep track of what you spend for an evening out? Are you sometimes surprised to find that you have very little money left when you get home? Danny wanted to pay more attention to where her money goes, so she decided to keep track of what she spent for an evening.

Problem 1.4

At the beginning of the evening, Danny had a twenty-dollar bill, five quarters, seven dimes, three nickels, and eight pennies.

A. Danny went to the Friday night school dance, which cost $2.50 to attend. How much money did she have left after paying for the dance?

B. After the dance, Danny and three friends bought a pizza for $6.99 and four soft drinks for 89¢ each. The bill for the pizza and drinks included a sales tax of 7%. How much was the bill? Show how you found your answer.

C. If Danny and her friends shared the cost of the pizza and drinks equally, how much was Danny's share of the bill?

D. On the way home, Danny stopped at a newsstand and bought a copy of *Stars and Planets* magazine for $2.50 plus 7% sales tax. How much had she spent for the evening?

E. How much money did Danny have left at the end of the evening?

■ Problem 1.4 Follow-Up

1. About what fraction of her money did Danny spend during the evening?

2. About what fraction of her money did Danny have left at the end of the evening?

3. About what percent of her money did Danny spend during the evening?

4. About what percent of her money did Danny have left?

As you work on these ACE questions, use your calculator whenever you need it.

Applications

1. Find three examples of advertisements, news reports, or other information in which percents are used. Store windows, newspapers, magazines, radio, and television are good places to look. Write down each example, or cut it out and tape it to your paper. For each example, describe how percents are used and what they mean.

2. Faaiz and Tat Ming go to a restaurant for dinner. Their meals total $13.75.

   a. The local sales tax is 5%. How much tax will be added to the bill?

   b. They want to leave a 15% tip based on the bill and the tax combined. How much should they leave? Explain.

   c. If Faaiz decides he should pay $2.75 more than Tat Ming because he ordered the more expensive dinner, how much should each pay? Explain.

3. Jeremy and Jessica are at a carnival.

   a. At the food stand, hot dogs cost 99¢ each plus 7% tax. How much will Jeremy and Jessica be charged for one hot dog?

   b. They stop at a ball-toss game. The sign reads, "Get three balls for 50¢ or six balls for 80¢." What percent would they save by buying one set of six balls instead of two sets of three balls? Explain.

4. a. Roller blades are on sale for 35% off the regular price. What fraction off is this discount?

   b. If the original price of roller blades is $124.99, what is the sale price?

   c. If a tax of 5% is computed on the sale price, what will the roller blades cost?

5. a. Ted has done $\frac{3}{10}$ of his homework. What percent is this?

   b. What percent does he still have to do?

6. In a survey, 75% of 400 parents said yes, they give their children fruit as a snack. How many answered yes to the survey?

7. In a survey, 50% of 150 kindergarten teachers said yes, they give their students crackers as a snack. How many answered yes to the survey?

8. In a survey, 50% of 50 grandparents said yes, they give their grandchildren candy as a snack. How many answered yes to the survey?

9. In a survey, 5% of 100 children said yes, they get popcorn as a snack. How many answered yes to the survey?

10. Four friends ordered a square pizza. Maryann said she wasn't hungry and only wanted 10% of the pizza. Bill was very hungry and said he would eat 50% of the pizza. Jon said he would eat 35%, and Kwan thought she could eat 15%. Will this be possible? Explain your reasoning.

11. Science fiction books at the Book Bonanza are marked $\frac{1}{3}$ off. What percent is this?

12. A certain bean plant grows 15% of its height each day. Express this percent growth as a decimal.

13. The purchase of a new mountain bike at Ike's Bikes requires 25% of the cost as a down payment. What fraction of the cost is this percent?

14. A fifty-cent piece is $\frac{50}{100}$ of a dollar, or half of a dollar, or 50% of a dollar, or $0.50.

   a. Find three different ways to represent 30% of a dollar.

   b. Find three different ways to represent 120% of a dollar.

In 15–17, list the smallest number of coins needed to make each amount.

15. 4% of a dollar

16. 20% of a dollar

17. 137% of a dollar

Connections

18. Anna, Brenda, and Carma each sent an entry to the Spartan Running Shoe contest. The Spartan Company advertised that they would award prizes for 1% of the total number of entries. They reported that 1600 entries were received. How many prizes did they award?

In 19–22, ink has been spilled on the page, covering up part of the fraction strips. Use what is showing to reason about each set of strips, and to find fractions equivalent to those marked.

19.

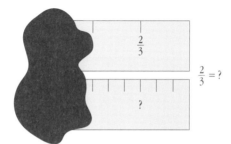

20.

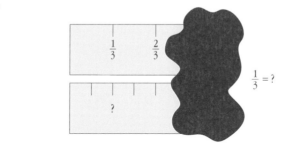

21.

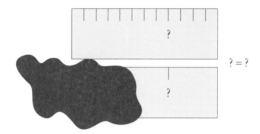

22.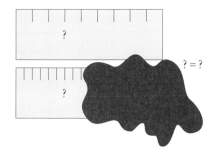

In 23–26, replace the question marks with numbers that will make the sentence true. There may be more than one solution. If so, show at least two solutions.

23. $\frac{4}{9} = \frac{?}{?}$

24. $\frac{?}{?} = \frac{3}{5}$

25. $\frac{?}{3} = \frac{8}{?}$

26. $\frac{5}{?} = \frac{?}{18}$

27. a. Write two fractions that are equivalent. Explain how you know that they are equivalent.

b. Look at the fractions you wrote in part a. Write two other fractions, one that is equivalent to your first fraction and one that is equivalent to your second fraction.

c. Are the four fractions you have written equivalent to each other? Why or why not?

28. a. Write two fractions that are not equivalent. Tell which is larger, and explain how you know.

b. Look at the fractions you wrote in part a. Write two other fractions, one that is *not* equivalent to your first fraction and one that is *not* equivalent to your second fraction. Show which fraction is larger in each pair.

c. Order the four fractions you have written from smallest to largest, and explain how you know the order is correct.

Extensions

29. Write a percent problem that involves discounts on food, cars, books, clothes, or other items. Solve your problem.

In 30–32, copy the number line (including all the labeled marks), and mark it to show where 1 would be. Rewrite each fraction, including 1, as a decimal and a percent.

30.

31.

32.

33. In a–d, replace the question marks with numbers that will make the sentence true.

a. $\frac{1}{3} = \frac{?}{9} = \frac{?}{6}$ **b.** $\frac{?}{18} = \frac{8}{12} = \frac{4}{?}$

c. $\frac{3}{?} = \frac{12}{?} = \frac{9}{?}$ **d.** $\frac{?}{3} = \frac{?}{21} = \frac{?}{7}$

e. Which problems have more than one possible answer? Why do you think this is so?

Mathematical Reflections

In this investigation, you solved problems that involved finding percents of numbers. You computed discounts, sale prices, tips, and sales taxes. These questions will help you summarize what you have learned:

1 If 1% of your bill for lunch at Pizza Muncho is 18¢, and you want to leave a 15% tip, how much money should you leave? How much money would you leave for a 20% tip? Explain how you got your answers and why your method works.

2 A sports outlet is having a 20% off sale on all merchandise. Describe a procedure you can use to find the sale price for any item in the store.

3 If you bought a calendar that was marked down by 30%, what percent of the original price did you pay? Explain your answer.

4 A store advertises an everyday discount of $\frac{1}{8}$ off the retail price of any item. Write an advertising slogan for the store that gives the everyday discount as a percent. Explain why the percent you have used in your slogan is equivalent to $\frac{1}{8}$.

Think about your answers to these questions, discuss your ideas with other students and your teacher, and then write a summary of your findings in your journal.

More About Percents

In the last investigation, you found percents of numbers. For example, you started with the price of an item and the percent discount offered on the item, and you computed how much money you would save.

In this investigation, you will begin with two numbers and find a percent that describes how they are related. For example, suppose that 50 out of 100 sixth graders surveyed said they liked to play basketball. You could say that 50% of the sixth graders surveyed liked to play basketball.

2.1 Finding Percents

It was easy to determine that 50% of the sixth graders liked to play basketball because exactly 100 people were surveyed, and percent means "out of 100." Often, though, surveys involve more than or less than 100 people.

Problem 2.1

A survey asked cat owners, Does your cat have bad breath? Out of the 200 cat owners surveyed, 80 answered yes to this question. What *percent* of the cat owners answered yes?

Try to find more than one way to solve this problem. For example, you might begin by asking yourself what *fraction* of the cat owners surveyed said their cats have bad breath. Be prepared to explain the different methods you use to solve the problem.

1. If you survey 500 cat owners, about how many would you expect to say their cats have bad breath? Explain your reasoning.

2. If you survey 75 cat owners, about how many would you expect to say their cats have bad breath? Explain your reasoning.

2.2 Finding a General Strategy

One of the powerful things about mathematics is that you can often find a way to solve one problem that will also work for solving similar problems.

Problem 2.2

Here are more questions that involve figuring out what percent of people have answered yes to a survey question. As you work on these questions, try to find a way to describe a general strategy you can use for solving these kinds of problems.

A. If 80 out of 400 cat owners surveyed said their cats have bad breath, what percent of the cat owners is this? Is this percent greater than, equal to, or less than the percent represented by 80 out of 200 cat owners? Explain.

B. If 120 out of 300 seventh graders surveyed said math is their favorite subject, what percent of these seventh graders is this?

C. If 30 out of 50 adults surveyed said they enjoy their jobs, what percent of these adults is this?

D. If 34 out of 125 sixth graders surveyed said they would like to try hang gliding, what percent of these sixth graders is this?

E. If 5 out of 73 middle-school students said they look forward to fire drills, what percent of these middle-school students is this?

F. Write an explanation for how to solve these kinds of problems.

■ **Problem 2.2 Follow-Up**

1. For each part of Problem 2.2, how would you find the *fraction* of people surveyed that answered in the given way? How does finding a fraction help you find a percent?

2. **a.** A pet store sells a new digestible mouthwash for cats. To promote the new product, the store is offering $0.50 off of the regular price of $2.00 for an 8-ounce bottle. Use the explanation you wrote in question 1 to find the percent of the discount.

   b. Change the dollar amounts in part a to numbers of pennies. Now find the percent discount on the mouthwash. How do your answers compare?

2.3 Clipping Coupons

Newspapers often have coupons for discounts on many different things. For example, the pet store mentioned in Problem 2.2 Follow-Up had a coupon for $1.50 off a 20-ounce bottle of mouthwash for cats. The regular price for the mouthwash is $5.00. Alicia wanted to figure out what percent discount this is. She thought about the problem this way:

"I need to find what percent $1.50 is of $5.00. I can think of these amounts in pennies. The fraction I want to represent as a percent is $\frac{150}{500}$, which is equivalent to $\frac{30}{100}$. As a decimal, this fraction is 0.3. This means that the discount is 30%!"

Coupons for cat mouthwash may not interest you, but you may be interested in coupons, like the one below, that give discounts for purchases of food at your favorite restaurant:

Problem 2.3

What percent discount do you get with the coupon above?

Try to find more than one way to solve this problem. Be prepared to explain the different methods you discover.

■ **Problem 2.3 Follow-Up**

1. For the sale below, estimate the percent discount you get. Explain your reasoning.

MOVIE

Regular price: $4.50
Today only: $4.00

TICKETS

2. For the sale below, estimate the percent discount you get. Explain your reasoning.

BIG SALE ON
BINOCULARS!
Regular price: $29.50
Now pay just: $17.70

3. The discount on a skateboard is $24.75, which is 25% of the original cost. What was the original cost?

4. The regular price for the sneakers that Kelly wants is $68.98. The sneakers are on sale for 20% off. A sales tax of 6% will be computed on the sale price. How much will Kelly pay for the shoes?

2.4 Making Circle Graphs

Circle graphs, or *pie charts,* are special kinds of graphs used to show how a whole (100%) is divided into several categories. For example, dog and cat owners who said their pets had bad breath were asked, Which of these methods do you use most frequently to take care of your pet's bad breath? Here are the results of the survey:

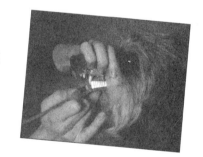

	Dog owners	Cat owners
Toothpaste	54%	53%
Mouthwash	16%	14%
Dental floss	7%	24%
Other	23%	9%
Total	**100%**	**100%**

Notice that when you add the percents in each column, you get a total of 100%.

This information is represented below in two circle graphs.

Methods Used by Dog Owners   **Methods Used by Cat Owners**

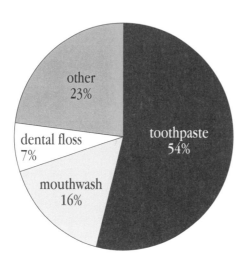 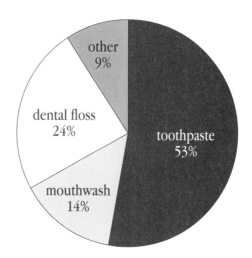

Problem 2.4

Study the circle graphs above. Use what you know about angle measures, circles, and percents to figure out how they were created. Then work on the problem below.

Cat and dog owners were asked, Do you let your pet lick your face? Here are the results of the survey:

	Cat owners	Dog owners
Yes	40%	75%
No	60%	25%
Total	**100%**	**100%**

Create two circle graphs to display this information.

Problem 2.4 Follow-Up

1. Cat and dog owners were asked, Does your pet sleep in the same room with you? The results are shown in the table. Make two circle graphs to display these results.

	Cat owners	Dog owners
Yes	73%	47%
No	27%	53%
Total	**100%**	**100%**

2. How do the answers of the cat owners and dog owners compare?

As you work on these ACE questions, use your calculator whenever you need it.

Applications

1. Suppose 43 out of 100 cat owners surveyed said their cats weigh under 10 pounds. What percent of cat owners surveyed is this?

2. Suppose 18 out of 200 race car owners surveyed said their cars are green. What percent of race car owners surveyed is this?

3. Suppose 15 out of 25 skydivers surveyed said they had never had a skydiving accident. What percent of skydivers surveyed is this?

4. Suppose 30 out of 40 private investigators surveyed said their jobs are exceedingly dull. What percent of private investigators surveyed is this?

5. What is 5% of 40? Show how you found your answer.

6. What is 75% of 80? Show how you found your answer.

7. What is 22% of 220? Show how you found your answer.

8. 5 is what percent of 40? Show how you found your answer.

9. 75 is what percent of 80? Show how you found your answer.

10. 22 is what percent of 220? Show how you found your answer.

11. In 1991, about 15 bike thefts were reported for every 100 people who owned bikes. What percent of the bike owners had their bikes stolen?

12. As part of a probability activity, Jack is counting the occurrence of different letters in a paragraph in his biology book. In the first 1000 letters in the paragraph, he found 50 b's. What percent of the letters were b's?

13. Estimate what percent discount Janey will receive if she buys the microscope kit advertised below. Explain.

MICROSCOPE KITS

Customers *usually* pay: $7.95
Students *save* by paying only: $6.76

14. The auto shop class conducted a survey to determine which math teacher's car was the most popular with the students. These were the results:

Ms. Grant's car   48 votes
Ms. Dole's car   35 votes
Mr. Manzinc's car   12 votes
Ms. Block's car   75 votes

a. What percent of the votes did Mr. Manzine's car receive? Explain.

b. What percent of the votes did Ms. Dole's car receive? Explain.

c. One student said Ms. Grant's car received 48% of the votes. Is he correct? Explain.

15. Bob, Sally, and Chi belong to an after-school youth group. They joined the group at different times after the beginning of school. The chart shows their attendance so far at the various events, including meetings, held by the youth group.

Member	Events attended since joined	Total events held since joined
Bob	20	30
Sally	11	18
Chi	7	12

a. If the attendance pattern of all three students remains about the same for the next 30 events, who will have the highest percent of attendance at the 30 events? Explain your reasoning.

b. Out of the 120 events planned for the rest of the year, how many would you expect each of the students to attend if they kept the same percent of attendance? Explain your reasoning.

16. a. Dog and cat owners were asked, How often do you feed your pet? The results are shown in the table below. Make two circle graphs of the results.

	Cat owners	Dog owners
Night only	4%	2%
Morning only	6%	10%
Morning and night	42%	46%
Anytime	48%	42%
Total	**100%**	**100%**

b. Compare the feeding patterns of dog owners to cat owners.

Connections

17. In a survey of 100 dog owners about their pets' habits, 39% said that their dogs eat bugs. How many dog owners surveyed said this?

18. When 300 tarantula owners were surveyed, 26% said they let their spiders crawl on them. How many tarantula owners surveyed said this?

19. In a survey of 80 students, 40% said they had a savings account of their own. How many students surveyed said this?

20. During a survey of 80 student artists, 6% said they had sold at least one of their works of art. How many students surveyed said this?

21. **a.** Janelle said, "The median divides a set of data in half." What does she mean?

   b. Randy added, "If the median divides a set of data in half, you always know what percent of the data is below the median and what percent of the data is above the median." Is Randy correct? Justify your answer.

22. In a–e, use the line plot to answer the question.

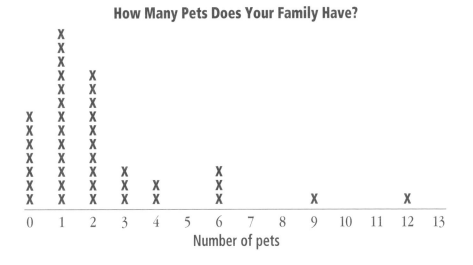

How Many Pets Does Your Family Have?

Number of pets

a. What percent of the 40 people surveyed have more than two pets? Explain how you found your answer.

b. What percent of the 40 people surveyed have fewer than three pets? Explain how you found your answer.

c. What is the median of the distribution?

d. What percent of the people surveyed are below the median?

e. What percent of the people surveyed are above the median?

Extensions

23. 80 is 40% of what number? Explain.

24. 220 is 20% of what number? Explain.

25. A circle graph is not always useful when you are working with percents. For example, when people are allowed to choose more than one answer to a survey question, the percents for the categories may add to *more than* 100%. For example, in one survey people were asked why they owned a pet. They were given several choices and were allowed to mark off more than one reason. Because multiple answers were allowed, the percents add to more than 100%.

	Dog owners	Cat owners
Love/companionship	88%	93%
Security	39%	0%
Protection	35%	0%
Entertainment	26%	33%
Catching rodents	0%	16%
Breeding (to make money)	16%	6%
Children grown/spouse died	4%	10%
Total	**208%**	**158%**

You can make a circle graph only when the percents add to 100%. When they add to more than 100%, you can make a bar graph to show the information.

a. Make bar graphs to display the data shown in the table. Before you make your bar graphs, think about these questions:

- What kind of data will you display in your graphs?
- What information will you show on the horizontal axis (the *x*-axis)?
- What information will you show on the vertical axis (the *y*-axis)?
- What scale will you use for the *y*-axis?

b. Write a paragraph comparing the responses of dog owners to cat owners in this survey.

In 26–30, replace the question marks with numbers that make the sentence true.

26. $\frac{6}{?} = \frac{18}{?} = \frac{?}{20}$

27. $\frac{12}{?} = \frac{?}{36} = \frac{?}{12}$

28. $\frac{2}{3} < \frac{?}{9}$

29. $\frac{2}{3} = \frac{?}{9}$

30. $\frac{2}{3} > \frac{?}{9}$

Mathematical Reflections

In this investigation, you studied situations for which you needed to find the percent one number is of another number so that you could describe the situation or compare it to another situation. These questions will help you summarize what you have learned:

1 Describe at least two ways to find what percent 30 is of 120. Explain why each method works.

2 Describe how to find what percent 34 is of 135. Explain your method.

3 Explain how you would find what part of a circle graph should be shaded to show 23%.

Think about your answers to these questions, discuss your ideas with other students and your teacher, and then write a summary of your findings in your journal.

INVESTIGATION 3

Estimating with Fractions and Decimals

Sometimes when you need to find an amount of something, you will not need or will not be able to get an exact answer. In these situations, you can estimate an answer. This investigation will give you practice in making estimates with fractions and decimals.

3.1 Getting Close

Getting Close is a game that will sharpen your skills at estimating with fractions and decimals. In *Bits and Pieces I*, we developed a set of *benchmarks* for estimating fractions and decimals. You learned to find which benchmark a number is nearest. Look at this set of benchmarks:

$$0 \qquad \frac{1}{4} \qquad \frac{1}{2} \qquad \frac{3}{4} \qquad 1 \qquad 1\frac{1}{4} \qquad 1\frac{1}{2} \qquad 1\frac{3}{4} \qquad 2$$

Which benchmark is $\frac{5}{8}$ nearest? Five eighths is larger than $\frac{1}{2}$, because it is larger than $\frac{4}{8}$. Five eighths is smaller than $\frac{3}{4}$, because it is smaller than $\frac{6}{8}$. In fact, $\frac{5}{8}$ is exactly halfway between $\frac{1}{2}$ and $\frac{3}{4}$.

Think about this!

How could you use benchmarks to help you quickly estimate the sum of two fractions? For example, think about this sum:

$$\frac{1}{8} + 1\frac{5}{7}$$

Is this sum larger or smaller than 2? Now, look at this sum:

$$\frac{1}{2} + \frac{5}{8}$$

Is this sum closest to 0, to 1, or to 2?

When you play Getting Close, you will use benchmarks and other methods to estimate the sum of two numbers.

Getting Close Rules

Getting Close is played by two to four players.

Materials
- A set of Getting Close game cards
- A set of three number squares—0, 1, and 2 (1 set per player)

Playing
- All players hold their 0, 1, and 2 number squares in their hands, hidden from view of the other players.

- The game cards are placed face down in a pile in the center of the table.

- For a *round of play,* one player turns over two game cards from the pile. Each player mentally estimates the sum of the numbers on the two game cards, and puts the number square (0, 1, or 2) he or she thinks is closest to the sum face down in the center of the table.

- After each player has played a number square, find the actual sum by using a calculator or some other method.

- The first player who put the correct number square in the center of the table collects the two game cards. If there is a tie, all players who tied get one game card. Players who have tied may take game cards from the deck if necessary.

- Each player who chose the wrong number square must return one game card (if he or she has one) to the bottom of the pile.

- The player who wins the round turns over the next two game cards.

- When all of the game cards have been used, the player with the most game cards wins.

Problem 3.1

Play Getting Close once or twice. Keep a record of the estimation strategies you find useful. You may find benchmarks, fraction strips, number lines, hundredths grids, or changing a fraction to a decimal or a decimal to a fraction helpful in making estimates. You may discover other ways of thinking that help. As you play the game, your group may use a calculator to check whether a player is correct— but not to estimate the sums!

■ Problem 3.1 Follow-Up

Describe or illustrate one estimation strategy that you found useful in the game.

3.2 Getting Even Closer

Now you will play the game Getting Even Closer, which requires you to estimate sums to the nearest 0.5. The rules are the same as for Getting Close, and the same game cards are used. However, each player will now have six number squares: 0, 0.5, 1, 1.5, 2, and 2.5.

Problem 3.2

Play Getting Even Closer once or twice. Keep a record of your strategies for estimating the sums. As before, your group may use a calculator to check whether a player is correct, but not to estimate the sums.

After a round of play, the player who won should explain the strategy he or she used to estimate the sum.

■ Problem 3.2 Follow-Up

1. a. The following fractions occur so often that it is useful to be able to recall their decimal and percent equivalents quickly:

$$\frac{1}{2} \quad \frac{1}{3} \quad \frac{1}{4} \quad \frac{2}{3} \quad \frac{3}{4} \quad \frac{1}{6} \quad \frac{1}{5}$$

For each of these important fractions, give the decimal and percent equivalents.

b. Draw a number line. On your number line, label the point corresponding to each fraction listed in part a.

2. Suppose you played Getting Close with only these game cards:

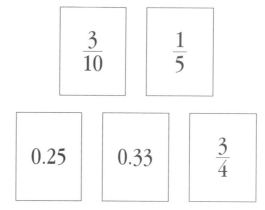

   a. What is the largest sum possible?

   b. What is the smallest sum possible?

3. a. If you add two numbers and the sum is closest to 1.5 (using the set of benchmarks 0, 0.5, 1, 1.5, 2, and 2.5), what is the largest the sum could actually be?

   b. If you add two numbers and the sum is closest to 1.5 (using the set of benchmarks 0, 0.5, 1, 1.5, 2, and 2.5), what is the smallest the sum could actually be?

As you work on these ACE questions, use your calculator whenever you need it.

Applications

1. Ask an adult to describe some situations in which a very close estimate is needed and some situations in which an estimate can just be "in the ballpark."

2. Ask an adult to describe some situations in which an overestimate is needed.

3. Ask an adult to describe some situations in which an underestimate is needed.

4. Many sewing patterns have a $\frac{5}{8}$-inch allowance for sewing the seam. Is this allowance closer to 0, $\frac{1}{2}$, or 1 inch? Explain your reasoning.

In 5–10, tell whether the fraction is closest to 0, $\frac{1}{2}$, or 1. Explain your reasoning.

5. $\frac{4}{9}$ 6. $\frac{9}{16}$

7. $\frac{4}{7}$ 8. $\frac{500}{1000}$

9. $\frac{5}{6}$ 10. $\frac{48}{100}$

In 11–19, find two fractions with a sum that is between the two given numbers.

11. 0 and 1   12. 0 and $\frac{1}{2}$ 13. $\frac{1}{2}$ and 1

14. 1 and 2   15. 1 and $1\frac{1}{2}$ 16. $1\frac{1}{2}$ and 2

17. 2 and 3   18. 2 and $2\frac{1}{2}$ 19. $2\frac{1}{2}$ and 3

In 20–23, the sum is a student's solution to the problem: "Find two fractions with a sum greater than $\frac{3}{4}$." Tell whether the solution is correct and explain your reasoning.

20. $\frac{1}{8} + \frac{2}{4}$ 21. $\frac{3}{6} + \frac{2}{4}$

22. $\frac{5}{12} + \frac{5}{6}$ 23. $\frac{5}{10} + \frac{3}{8}$

In 24–29, tell whether the number is closest to 0, 0.5, 1, or 1.5, and explain your reasoning.

24. 0.67

25. 1.15

26. 0.000999

27. 0.78

28. 0.26

29. 1.90

30. Janine is having seven friends over for breakfast. Of the eight people who will be eating breakfast, six like orange juice best, and two prefer grapefruit juice. Both kinds of juice cost $2.89 for a half gallon, $2.09 for a quart ($\frac{1}{4}$ of a gallon), and $1.29 for a pint ($\frac{1}{8}$ of a gallon). How many of each size container of each type of juice should Janine buy? Use estimation to help you decide. Explain your reasoning.

In 31–34, fill in each blank with 1, 2, or 3 to form decimal numbers so that each sum is as close as possible to the given number. You may use the same digit twice in one number. For example, you may write 0.33. The symbol ≈ means "is approximately equal to."

31. 0.___ ___ + 0.___ ___ ≈ 0.5

32. 0.___ ___ + 0.___ ___ ≈ 0.25

33. 0.___ ___ + 0.___ ___ ≈ 0.75

34. 0.___ ___ + 0.___ ___ ≈ 0.4

Connections

35. If you sleep about 30% of each day, estimate how many hours you have slept by the time you are 12 years old. Explain your reasoning.

36. Order these decimals from largest to smallest.

5.693   5.639   5.96   5.67   5.599

37. Julio is at the grocery store near his apartment. He has $10.00, but no calculator or paper and pencil. At right is a list of the items he would like to buy.

Use mental computation and estimation to answer questions a–c.

Item	Price
Milk	$2.47
Eggs	$1.09
Cheese	$1.95
Bread	$0.68
Honey	$1.19
Cereal	$3.25
Avocado	$0.50

a. Can Julio buy all the items with the money he has? Explain your reasoning.

b. If Julio had only $5.00, what could he buy? Give two possibilities.

c. What different items could Julio buy to come as close as possible to spending $5.00?

In 38–40, copy the figure onto your paper and shade about $\frac{1}{3}$ of the figure.

38.

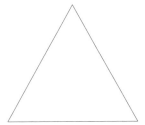

39.

40.

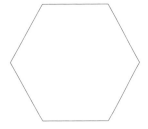

In 41–43, copy the figure onto your paper and shade about $\frac{1}{4}$ of the figure.

41.

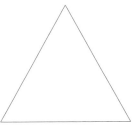

42.

43.

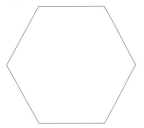

44. Here is a map of the area where Seth is hiking.

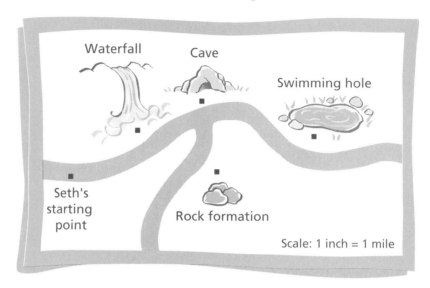

a. The distance from where Seth starts to the waterfall is $\frac{7}{8}$ of an inch. The distance from the waterfall to the mouth of the cave is $\frac{3}{4}$ of an inch. Will Seth's trip to the waterfall and then the cave be shorter or longer than a mile? Explain.

b. When Seth gets to the cave, he decides to take a side trip to see the rock formation. On the map, the rock formation is about 75% of an inch from the cave. After visiting the rock formation, Seth retraces his steps to return to the main trail. When he gets back to the main trail, about how many miles has he hiked since he started his travels?

c. After the side trip, Seth heads for the swimming hole. On the map, this is about $1\frac{1}{4}$ inches from the cave. When he arrives at the swimming hole, about how many miles has he walked altogether?

d. Seth's buddy, who lives on the other side of the swimming hole, meets him for a swim. Late in the day, they retrace Seth's steps to where Seth started. They do not make the side trip to the rock formation. About how many miles has Seth now walked altogether?

In 45–48, tell what percent of the whole rectangle each numbered section represents.

45.

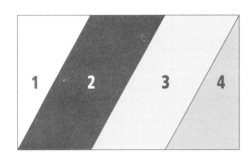

46.

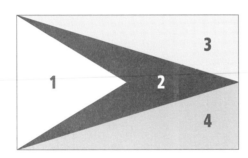

47.

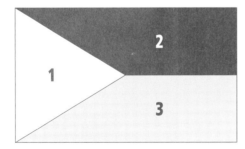

48.

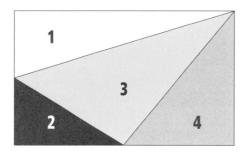

49. The table below lists the abundance of the eight most common elements in the earth's crust.

Element	Portion of earth's crust
Oxygen	0.4660
Iron	0.0500
Silicon	0.2772
Aluminum	0.0813
Sodium	0.0283
Calcium	0.0363
Potassium	0.0259
Magnesium	0.0209

a. Order the elements in the earth's crust from most abundant to least abundant.

b. Estimate how much of the earth's crust is made up of the *three* most abundant elements.

c. About what percent of the crust is made up of these three elements?

d. About what percent of the crust is made up of the three least abundant elements listed in the table?

In 50–54, find a decimal number in the given interval.

50. between $\frac{1}{2}$ and 1

51. between $\frac{1}{3}$ and $\frac{1}{2}$

52. between $\frac{1}{4}$ and $\frac{1}{3}$

53. between $\frac{1}{5}$ and $\frac{1}{4}$

54. between $\frac{1}{6}$ and $\frac{1}{5}$

55. In 50–54, can you find another decimal in each interval? Why or why not?

In 56 and 57, ink has been spilled on the page, concealing part of the fraction strips. Use what is showing to reason about each pair of strips, and find the equivalent fractions indicated by the question marks.

56.

57.

Mathematical Reflections

In this investigation, you played two games that helped you develop strategies for estimating the sum of two fractions or decimals. These questions will help you summarize what you have learned:

1 Describe one strategy that you found helpful in estimating sums. Explain why it was helpful to you.

2 If the two game cards turned up are both between 0.5 and 0.75, what is the smallest the sum could be? What is the largest the sum could be? Explain your reasoning.

3 If you are estimating the sum of two numbers and one is nearest the benchmark $\frac{1}{4}$ and the other is nearest the benchmark $1\frac{1}{2}$, what estimate would you give? Why?

Think about your answers to these questions, discuss your ideas with other students and your teacher, and then write a summary of your findings in your journal.

Adding and Subtracting Fractions

Knowing how to combine and remove quantities is a skill that is helpful for understanding the world around you. The mathematical names for combining and removing are adding and subtracting. For example, if you owned two lots of land and you bought another half a lot, you could combine the two lots and the half lot to determine that you owned $2 + \frac{1}{2}$, or $2\frac{1}{2}$, lots of land.

The problems in this investigation require you to add and subtract fractions. As you work on these problems, use what you have learned in earlier investigations about finding equivalent fractions and rewriting fractions as decimals.

4.1 Dividing Land

When Tupelo township was founded, the land was divided into sections that could be farmed. Each *section* is a square that is 1 mile long on each edge—that is, each section is 1 square mile of land. There are 640 acres of land in a 1-square-mile section.

The diagram on the next page shows two *adjacent* sections of land, sections 18 and 19. Each section is divided among several owners. The diagram shows the part of the land each person owns.

Problem 4.1

Determine what fraction of a section each person owns. Explain your reasoning.

■ Problem 4.1 Follow-Up

Determine how many acres of land each person owns. Explain your reasoning.

Section 18   **Section 19**

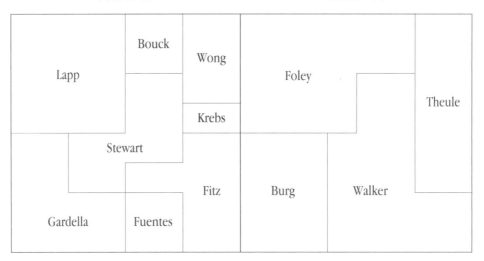

4.2 Redrawing the Map

As time goes by, some people in sections 18 and 19 want to sell their farms, and other people want to buy more land to expand their farms. In the real world, transactions to buy and sell land occur every day.

Problem 4.2

Some of the owners of land in sections 18 and 19 sold their land to other people who already owned land in these sections. The clues below describe the results of several transactions.

Clue 1 When all the sales are completed, four people—Theule, Fuentes, Wong, and Gardella—own all of the land in the two sections.

Clue 2 Theule bought from one person and now owns land equivalent to $\frac{1}{2}$ of one section.

Clue 3 Fuentes bought from three people and now owns the equivalent of $\frac{13}{32}$ of one section.

Clue 4 Gardella now owns the equivalent of $\frac{1}{2}$ of a section.

Clue 5 Wong now owns all of the rest of the land in the two sections.

Clue 6 Each of the four owners can walk around all of their land without having to cross onto another person's land.

A. Use the clues to determine what transactions took place. Determine exactly which pieces of land Theule, Fuentes, Wong, and Gardella bought, and explain how you know you are correct.

B. Draw a new map of the two sections, outlining the land belonging to each of the four owners. Tell how many acres each person now owns.

■ Problem 4.2 Follow-Up

After a few years, Fuentes wants to acquire more land to put in new pastures for his livestock. Gardella sells $\frac{1}{2}$ of a section to Fuentes, Theule sells $\frac{1}{8}$ of a section to Fuentes, and Wong sells $\frac{1}{16}$ of a section to Fuentes. What fraction of a section does each person now own?

4.3 Pirating Pizza

In this problem, you can use what you have discovered about adding and subtracting fractions to make sense of the havoc that the infamous Pizza Pirate is causing! As you work on the problem, look for patterns that can help you to solve it.

Problem 4.3

Courtney's class made a gigantic square pizza for a class party to be held the day after the final exam. They made it a week before the party so they would have time to study. To keep the pizza fresh, they stored it in the cafeteria freezer.

Unfortunately, the notorious Pizza Pirate was lurking in the area. That night, the Pizza Pirate disguised himself as a janitor, tiptoed into the cafeteria, and gobbled down half of the pizza! On the second night, he ate half of what was left of the pizza. Each night after that, he crept in and ate half of the pizza that remained.

After the final exam, Courtney's class went to get their pizza to start their celebration—and were stunned by what they found!

What fraction of the pizza was left for the party?

To help you answer this question, make a table or chart showing

- the fraction of the pizza the Pizza Pirate ate each day
- the fraction of the pizza he had eaten so far at the end of each day
- the fraction of the pizza that remained at the end of each day

Write a summary of how your group solved this problem. Draw any diagrams that will help you to show your thinking.

1. a. Make a graph of the total amount eaten so far by the Pizza Pirate for each of the seven days.

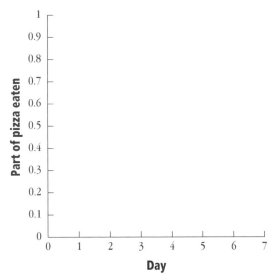

b. Make a graph of how much pizza remains at the end of the day for each of the seven days.

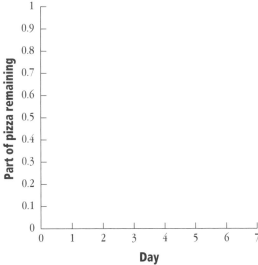

c. How are the graphs you made in parts a and b related?

2. If the students canceled the party and left the pizza in the freezer for a long time, would the Pizza Pirate ever eat all of the pizza?

4.4 Designing Algorithms

To become skillful at handling situations that call for the addition and subtraction of fractions, you need a good plan for carrying out your computations. In mathematics, a plan—or a series of steps—for doing a computation is called an **algorithm.** For an algorithm to be useful, each step should be clear and precise so that other people will be able to carry out the steps and get correct answers.

In this problem, you will work with your group to develop algorithms for adding and subtracting fractions. Your group may develop more than one algorithm for each computation. What is important is that each member of your group understands and feels comfortable with at least one algorithm for adding fractions and at least one algorithm for subtracting fractions.

Problem 4.4

Work with your group to develop at least one algorithm for adding fractions and at least one algorithm for subtracting fractions. You might want to look back over the first three problems in this investigation and discuss how each person in your group thought about them. Look for ideas that you think will help you develop algorithms for adding and subtracting fractions that will always work, even with mixed numbers.

Test your algorithms on a few problems, such as these:

$$\frac{5}{8} + \frac{7}{8} \qquad \frac{3}{5} + \frac{5}{3} \qquad 3\frac{3}{4} + 7\frac{2}{9}$$

$$\frac{3}{4} - \frac{1}{8} \qquad 5\frac{4}{6} - 2\frac{1}{3} \qquad \frac{5}{6} - \frac{1}{4}$$

If necessary, make adjustments to your algorithms until you think they will work all the time. Write up a final version of each algorithm. Make sure they are neat and precise so others can follow them.

■ Problem 4.4 Follow-Up

1. Exchange your addition algorithm with that of another group. Test the other group's plan. Write a paragraph explaining how your algorithm and the other group's algorithm are alike and how they are different.

2. Exchange your subtraction algorithm with that of another group (a different group from the group you exchanged with in part 1). Test the other group's plan. Write a paragraph explaining how your algorithm and the other group's algorithm are alike and how they are different.

As you work on these ACE questions, use your calculator whenever you need it.

Applications

1. A local magazine sells advertising space. It charges advertisers according to the fraction of a page their ad will fill.

    a. For page 20 in the magazine, advertisers have purchased $\frac{1}{8}$ of the page and $\frac{1}{16}$ of the page. What fraction of the page will be used for ads? What fraction of the page will remain for other uses? Explain your reasoning.

    b. The Cool Sub Shop is having its grand opening and has purchased several ads. They buy three $\frac{1}{4}$-page ads, four $\frac{1}{8}$-page ads, and ten $\frac{1}{16}$-page ads. What is the total amount of space that they have bought? Explain your reasoning.

    c. The magazine wants to make $160 for each page of advertising sold. What might the magazine charge for each size ad if ads can be any of the following sizes: $\frac{1}{32}$, $\frac{1}{16}$, $\frac{1}{8}$, $\frac{1}{4}$, $\frac{1}{2}$, or a whole page? Explain your reasoning.

    d. Using the pricing scheme you developed in part c, what would the bill for the Cool Sub Shop be for the ads they purchased in part b? Explain your reasoning.

    e. For an upcoming issue, a local promoter has purchased a total of $2\frac{3}{4}$ pages of ads to promote two concerts. Now, one of the concerts must be canceled because the lead guitarist broke her finger. The promoter calls to cancel $1\frac{5}{8}$ pages of ads for that concert. How much advertising space does the promoter want to keep? Explain your reasoning.

    f. The senior class is having a fund-raiser to help raise money for their senior trip. They have $80 dollars to spend on advertising. Geraldo says they can purchase two $\frac{1}{8}$-page ads and four $\frac{1}{16}$-page ads for their money. According to your answer to part c, is he correct? Explain your reasoning.

    g. Give four different sets of ad sizes that the senior class could purchase with their $80 (using your pricing scheme from part c). Show why your answers work.

2. The Pizza Pirate and a friend broke into the school cafeteria and ate part of the huge sheet cake that was being stored for a party. The Pizza Pirate ate $\frac{1}{16}$ of the cake, and the accomplice ate $\frac{1}{32}$ of the cake. How much cake was left?

3. If you eat $\frac{3}{4}$ of a pizza and then eat $\frac{1}{8}$ of another pizza of the same size, how much of a whole pizza have you eaten altogether?

4. On the stock market report yesterday, the price of a stock that Ms. Jennings is watching was $27\frac{3}{4}$ dollars. Today the stock is reported at $26\frac{1}{8}$ dollars. How much did the stock price decline?

5. Ms. Jennings is watching another stock. These are the prices reported for a week in March: $1\frac{15}{16}$ on Monday, $2\frac{1}{8}$ on Tuesday, $2\frac{3}{8}$ on Wednesday, $2\frac{3}{16}$ on Thursday, and $2\frac{1}{4}$ on Friday. For each day of the week, beginning with Tuesday, how much did the stock go up or down?

In 6–9, tell which sum or difference is larger. Show your work.

6. $\frac{2}{3} + \frac{5}{6}$ or $\frac{3}{4} + \frac{4}{5}$

7. $\frac{7}{6} - \frac{2}{3}$ or $\frac{3}{5} - \frac{5}{10}$

8. $\frac{1}{4} + \frac{5}{6}$ or $\frac{1}{5} + \frac{7}{8}$

9. $\frac{1}{16} + \frac{1}{12}$ or $\frac{5}{4} - \frac{4}{5}$

Connections

In 10–15, replace the question mark with a number that will make the sentence true.

10. $\frac{3}{12} = \frac{?}{8}$

11. $\frac{?}{4} = \frac{6}{8}$

12. $\frac{1}{2} = \frac{?}{12}$

13. $\frac{?}{12} = \frac{2}{3}$

14. $\frac{?}{8} = \frac{14}{16}$

15. $\frac{5}{12} = \frac{10}{?}$

In 16–18, ink has spilled on the page, obscuring part of the fraction strips. Use what is showing to reason about each set of strips and to find the equivalent fractions indicated by the question marks.

16.

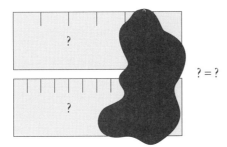

? = ?

17.

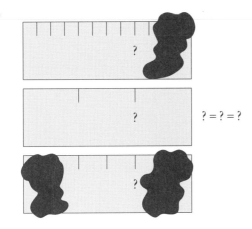

? = ? = ?

18.

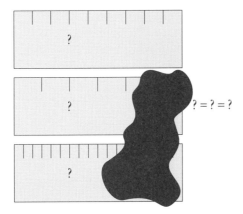

? = ? = ?

In 19–22, insert <, =, or > to make a true statement.

19. 18.156 _____ 18.17

20. 3.184 _____ 31.84

21. 5.78329 _____ 5.78239

22. 4.0074 _____ 4.0008

In 23–26, express the fraction as a decimal.

23. $\frac{3}{5}$

24. $\frac{18}{12}$

25. $\frac{5}{8}$

26. $\frac{15}{16}$

Extensions

27. **a.** Find three numbers for the denominators to make the sentence true.

$$\frac{1}{?} - \frac{1}{?} = \frac{1}{?}$$

b. Can you find another set of numbers that works?

Mathematical Reflections

In this investigation, you explored ways to add and subtract fractions. These questions will help you summarize what you have learned:

1. Describe how you can add or subtract two fractions that have the same denominator. Explain why your method makes sense.

2. Describe and illustrate with an example your algorithm for adding two fractions that have different denominators. Do the same for your algorithm for subtracting two fractions with different denominators.

3. Describe how you can use what you know about adding and subtracting fractions to add or subtract mixed numbers.

Think about your answers to these questions, discuss your ideas with other students and your teacher, and then write a summary of your findings in your journal.

Finding Areas and Other Products

Sometimes rather than adding or subtracting fractions, you need to multiply them. For example, suppose you are taking inventory at the sporting goods store where you work. There are $13\frac{1}{2}$ boxes of footballs in the stock room, and there are 12 footballs in a full box. How can you find the total number of footballs without opening all the boxes? Or, suppose $\frac{1}{4}$ of a pizza was left over and you ate $\frac{1}{2}$ of this amount. How can you find the total amount of pizza you ate?

In this investigation, you will see how you can relate what you already know about multiplication to situations involving fractions. Remember, to make sense of a situation, you can draw a model or change a fraction to an equivalent fraction or an equivalent form.

5.1 Selling Brownies

Paulo and Paula are tending the brownie booth at the school fair. All evening long they have run into interesting situations in which they have to find fractional parts of other fractions.

Think about this!

What operation is called for when you find a fractional part of another fraction: $+$, $-$, $\times$, or $\div$? For example, how much is $\frac{1}{2}$ of $\frac{1}{4}$? How could you write this problem using a mathematics operation sign?

Let's look at some of the problems Paulo and Paula had to solve while they were selling brownies.

Problem 5.1

The brownies are baked in square pans, and they are sold as fractional parts of a pan. A whole pan of brownies costs $24 dollars. The cost of any fractional part of a pan is that fraction of $24.

A. One pan of brownies was $\frac{2}{3}$ full. Mr. Sims bought $\frac{1}{2}$ of what was in the pan. What fraction of a full pan did Mr. Sims buy? How much did he pay?

B. Paulo's aunt Serena asked to buy $\frac{3}{4}$ of what was left in another pan. The pan was half full. How much of a whole pan did Aunt Serena buy? How much did she pay?

■ Problem 5.1 Follow-Up

For A and B above, draw a picture to show what each brownie pan looked like before Mr. Sims and Aunt Serena bought part of what remained. Then draw a picture that shows how much of each pan the customer got and how much was left. Mark your drawings so that someone else can easily see what fraction of the pan each customer bought.

Model of a Brownie Pan

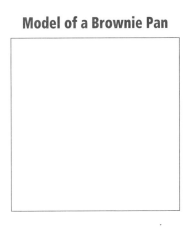

Use the drawings to check your computations in A and B for the fraction of the brownie pan and the price each customer paid.

Discounting Brownies

There are many occasions in which you will want to find a fraction times a fraction or a fraction times a whole number. When you solve problems involving multiplication with fractions, it helps to remember that finding a fraction *times* a number is the same as finding a fraction *of* a number. It is also helpful to draw models to show fractions and fraction operations.

At the brownie booth, a customer wanted to buy $\frac{1}{3}$ of a pan that was $\frac{1}{3}$ full. Paula said that they had to find $\frac{1}{3}$ of $\frac{1}{3}$. Paulo said that this is the same as $\frac{1}{3} \times \frac{1}{3}$. They decided to make a drawing to figure out how much the customer would get.

First, they made a drawing to show how much was in the pan:

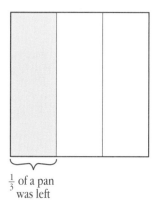

$\frac{1}{3}$ of a pan was left

Then, they showed how much the customer wanted, which was $\frac{1}{3}$ of $\frac{1}{3}$ of a pan:

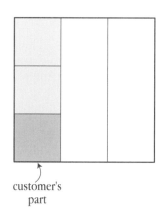

customer's part

They extended the horizontal lines to form nine equal parts. They then figured out that the customer would buy $\frac{1}{9}$ of a pan:

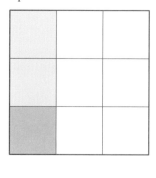

From inspecting their drawing, Paula and Paulo figured out that they should charge the customer $\frac{1}{9}$ of $24, or $2.67.

Think about this!

Why does it make sense that $\frac{1}{3}$ of $\frac{1}{3}$, or $\frac{1}{3} \times \frac{1}{3}$, is $\frac{1}{9}$?

Problem 5.2

The school fair was almost over. Paulo and Paula wanted to sell all the remaining brownies in a hurry, so they decided to offer a discount of 20% on all sales. They had $2\frac{1}{4}$ pans of brownies left. Remember, they originally sold a pan of brownies for $24.

Mr. Vargas offered to buy half of all that they had left.

A. How much will Mr. Vargas purchase?

B. How much should Paulo and Paula charge Mr. Vargas?

■ **Problem 5.2 Follow-Up**

When Mr. Vargas got his bill, he realized he had only $20 in his wallet, so he said, "I guess I'll only buy $\frac{1}{3}$ of what you have left."

1. Now how much will Mr. Vargas buy?

2. Can he afford this much? Explain your reasoning.

Buying the Biggest Lot

In the area where Miguel lives, land is expensive because many people want to live there. The lots for houses are small compared to the lots needed for farmland.

Miguel's mother builds and sells houses. She wants to buy a piece of land in their area on which to build several houses. There are two large lots for sale. One is a rectangular plot that is $\frac{3}{8}$ of a mile by $\frac{2}{3}$ of a mile. The other is a square plot that is $\frac{2}{5}$ of a mile by $\frac{2}{5}$ of a mile.

Problem 5.3

A. Which lot should Miguel's mother buy if she wants the biggest lot? Explain your reasoning.

B. If land in this area sells for $750,000 a square mile, about how much should Miguel's mother expect to pay?

■ Problem 5.3 Follow-Up

Miguel's mother has an idea for a beautiful trailer park. The trailer park would have lots of open areas for children to play in and a set of shops. She finds a farm for sale that is $1\frac{1}{4}$ miles $\times 2\frac{1}{5}$ miles. The farm has a pretty lake and lots of trees. She thinks it would be perfect for her trailer park.

1. How many square miles does the farm cover?

2. If land costs $750,000 a square mile, how much should she expect to pay?

3. If Miguel's mother receives a 7% discount because she is buying a large lot, how much will she have to pay?

Designing a Multiplication Algorithm

In Investigation 4, you wrote algorithms for adding and subtracting fractions. Recall that an *algorithm* is a plan, or a series of steps, for doing a computation. In this problem, you will work with your group to develop an algorithm for multiplying fractions.

Your group may develop more than one algorithm. What is important is that each member of your group understands and feels comfortable with at least one algorithm for multiplying fractions. Remember, for an algorithm to be useful, each step should be clear and precise so that other people will be able to carry out the steps and get correct answers.

Problem 5.4

Work with your group to develop at least one algorithm for multiplying fractions. You might want to look back over the first three problems in this investigation and discuss how each person in your group thought about them. Look for ideas that you think will help you develop an algorithm for multiplying fractions that will always work, even with mixed numbers.

Test your algorithm on a few problems, such as these:

$$\frac{1}{5} \times 25 \qquad 24 \times \frac{2}{3} \qquad \frac{5}{8} \times 12$$

$$\frac{3}{8} \times \frac{3}{4} \qquad \frac{1}{2} \times 2\frac{2}{3} \qquad 3\frac{1}{3} \times 2\frac{4}{5}$$

If necessary, make adjustments to your algorithm until you think it will work all the time. Write up a final version of the algorithm. Make sure it is neat and precise so others can follow it.

■ Problem 5.4 Follow-Up

Exchange your algorithm with that of another group. Test the other group's plan. Write a paragraph explaining how your algorithm and the other group's algorithm are alike and how they are different.

As you work on these ACE questions, use your calculator whenever you need it.

Applications

1. Ms. Guerdin owns $\frac{4}{5}$ of a section of land in Tupelo township. She wants to sell $\frac{2}{3}$ of her land to her neighbor. What fraction of a section does she want to sell?

2. **a.** Sarah uses balsa wood to build airplane models. After completing a model, she had a strip of balsa wood measuring $\frac{7}{8}$ of a yard left over. Shawn wants to buy half of the strip from Sarah. What fraction of a yard does Shawn want to buy?

b. If Sarah paid $2.00 for each yard, how much should she charge Shawn for the strip he buys?

3. A recipe for a large batch of cookies calls for $3\frac{1}{4}$ cups of flour. Amos wants to make half of a batch of cookies. How much flour should he use?

4. Murphy's department store is having a two-week sale during which all prices are reduced by $\frac{1}{3}$. Ophelia wants to buy the following items for her new apartment:

Item	Regular price
Vacuum cleaner	$120
Microwave oven	$240
Television	$330
4 CDs	$15 each
2 Speakers	$75 each

a. Ophelia has $500 saved for the purchases. Can she buy everything on her list?

b. There is a 5% sales tax. What is the most Ophelia could spend and on which items?

5. Rubin and Lea went to the amusement park on Saturday. Lea spent $\frac{1}{2}$ of her money, and Rubin spent $\frac{1}{4}$ of his money. Is it possible for Rubin to have spent more money than Lea? Explain your reasoning.

6. Mr. Jones' garden has an area of 21 square meters. He wants to increase its size by $\frac{1}{2}$. Draw a picture to show what his new garden might look like. Be sure to give the new area and dimensions, and show your reasoning.

7. Find a fraction and a whole number with a product that is a whole number.

8. Find a fraction and a whole number with a product less than $\frac{1}{2}$.

9. Find a fraction and a whole number with a product between $\frac{1}{2}$ and 1.

10. Find a fraction and a whole number with a product greater than 1.

Connections

11. Write a fraction between $\frac{1}{2}$ and $\frac{2}{3}$. Explain how you know your fraction is between $\frac{1}{2}$ and $\frac{2}{3}$.

12. The following table shows the number of people surveyed that intend to vote for each of the candidates for president. Make a circle graph for this data.

Candidate	Expected votes
Murningham	31
Graves	58
McKane	91

13. Inflation has caused a store owner to decide that she must increase all prices by 8%. What should she charge for the following items?

Item	Current price
basketball	$30
skateboard	$50
roller blades	$110
tennis racket	$75

In 14–16, insert <, >, or = to make the statement true.

14. $\frac{3}{5}$ —— $\frac{7}{8}$

15. $\frac{12}{15}$ —— $\frac{3}{4}$

16. $\frac{5}{8}$ —— $\frac{10}{16}$

17. Order these decimals from greatest to least.

0.302   0.1   0.099   0.167   0.32   0.4

Extensions

18. The Pizza Pirate has been up to new tricks. The archery club put two pizzas in the freezer for a party. Of the two pizzas, the Pizza Pirate ate $\frac{1}{2}$ of a pizza, then $\frac{1}{3}$ of a pizza, then $\frac{1}{4}$ of a pizza, and then $\frac{1}{6}$ of a pizza. How much pizza is left?

19. On a map of the city of Detroit, the library is $\frac{5}{12}$ of an inch from the post office. On the map, 1 inch represents 5 miles.

   a. What fraction of an inch represents 1 mile?

   b. How far apart are the post office and the library?

20. While traveling in Mexico, Samantha found some beautiful ceramic tiles. The tiles are square, $6\frac{1}{2}$ inches on each side. Samantha wants to buy enough tiles to cover the floor of her sun room. The sun room is also square, 108 inches on each side. How many tiles does Samantha need?

Mathematical Reflections

In this investigation, you explored situations in which you need to find a fraction of another fraction or a fraction of a whole number. You discovered that $\frac{2}{3}$ *of* $\frac{1}{2}$ is the same as $\frac{2}{3} \times \frac{1}{2}$. These questions will help you summarize what you have learned:

1 You can model the product of whole numbers by thinking of multiplication as finding area. For example, you can think of 6×7 as the area of a rectangle with dimensions of 6 and 7. Describe and show how you can mark a square to show $\frac{2}{3} \times \frac{1}{2}$.

2 Look back over all of the examples of multiplying fractions—or finding a fractional part of another fraction—that you worked with in this investigation. What patterns do you see that helped you develop an algorithm for multiplying fractions?

3 When you multiply two whole numbers, the product is larger than the factors. Is the product of two fractions larger than the fractions? Explain your reasoning.

Think about your answers to these questions, discuss your ideas with other students and your teacher, and then write a summary of your findings in your journal.

Computing with Decimals

Nearly every day of your life, you use or interpret decimal quantities. Because our system of currency is based on the decimal system, you deal with decimals every time you buy something. You use decimals when you measure things in metric units. When you read the newspaper, you often have to interpret statements that involve decimal numbers such as, "The new baseball stadium will cost 7.5 million dollars." or "The average working week in Finland is 38.1 hours."

The problems in this investigation involve adding, subtracting, and multiplying decimals. As you work through the problems, you will learn to make sense of operations with decimals.

6.1 Buying School Supplies

The School Supply game will give you practice in estimating and calculating with decimals. The game involves the prices of items at a school store.

Items Sold at the School Store

Divider page	$0.07	Roll of tape	$0.84
Pencil	$0.28	Pen	$0.98
Eraser	$0.35	Highlighter	$1.05
Note paper	$0.42	Notebook	$2.24
Ruler	$0.70	Scissors	$3.15

School Supply Game Board

$2.24	$1.33	$0.35	$2.31	$1.68	$0.07
$3.43	$0.28	$3.08	$2.59	$1.05	$1.47
$1.26	$1.75	$1.12	$1.61	$1.54	$1.96
$1.40	$3.57	$2.80	$1.89	$0.91	$2.66
$2.03	$0.84	$2.87	$2.73	$0.70	$2.52
$3.15	$0.77	$2.45	$0.98	$0.63	$0.42

Rules for the School Supply Game

Materials
- Labsheet 6.1 (1 per pair)
- Markers, such as squares of paper, marked with each player's initials (about 15 per person)

Playing
- Each player begins each turn assuming he or she has $4.20.

- In turn, each player makes up an addition, subtraction, or multiplication problem that uses the prices of some of the items from the school store. (Assume there is no sales tax.)

- If the answer to the problem is on the grid, the player who made up the problem covers the answer with one of his or her markers. If the answer is not on the grid, the player does not get to cover a square, and the next player takes a turn.

- The first player with four markers in a row—horizontally, vertically, or diagonally—wins the game.

Problem 6.1

Play the School Supply game once or twice with your partner. Keep track of any strategies you find that help you win the game.

■ Problem 6.1 Follow-Up

1. If you wanted to spend as much of your $4.20 as possible on rulers, how many rulers could you buy and how much money would you have left?

2. Tell what operations you used to do question 1, and explain why you used each operation.

6.2 Moving Decimal Points

In a decimal number, the location of the decimal point tells you the place value of every digit in the number. For example, in the numbers 236.5 and 23.65, the 2, 3, 6, and 5 mean different things. The 2 in the first number means 2 hundreds; in the second number, it means 2 tens.

In this problem you will explore the possible sums and differences you can make with the same two sets of digits. You might be surprised by all the possibilities you can make just by changing the location of the decimal point!

To keep the number of possibilities reasonable, the constraint is added that you may place the decimal point just before, between, or just after the given digits. After placing the decimal point, you may add zeros only if they do not change the value of your number. For example, using the numbers 2, 3, 6, and 5, the numbers 0.002365 and 236,500 are not allowed, but 2.3650 is allowed.

Think about this!

Alice is trying to create different sums by moving the decimal points in two numbers: 236 and 89. Here is her work so far:

a.	**b.**	**c.**	**d.**
236	23.6	23.6	23.6
+ 89	+ 8.9	+89.0	+ 0.089
325	32.5	112.6	23.689

Bill says that the 0 added in problem c is all right, but the 0 added after the decimal point in problem d does not fit the constraint. Bill is correct. Why?

Bill says that she could have written this problem:

23.60
+ 0.89
24.49

Why does Bill's problem fit the constraints?

Problem 6.2

Work with the digits 2365 and 894. You may insert a decimal point just before, between, or just after the given set of digits, but you cannot change the order of the digits. After placing the decimal point, you may add zeros only if they do not change the value of your number.

A. Find ways to insert decimal points so you get five different *sums* using these two numbers.

B. Find ways to insert decimal points so you get five different *differences* using these two numbers.

C. What is the largest sum that you can make that fits the constraints of the problem? What is the smallest sum?

D. What is the largest difference that you can make that fits the constraints of the problem? What is the smallest difference?

■ **Problem 6.2 Follow-Up**

Suppose you can put the digits *in any order* and insert a decimal point at any position, but you cannot add zeros after a decimal point in front of the digits.

1. What is the largest sum you can make? What is the smallest sum?

2. What is the largest difference you can make? What is the smallest difference?

6.3 Multiplying Decimals

You can think of decimals as fractions with denominators of 10, 100, 1000, and so forth. For example, $\frac{1}{10}$ can be written as 0.1 and $\frac{37}{100}$ can be written as 0.37. To write $\frac{2}{5}$ as a decimal, first rewrite it as the equivalent fraction $\frac{4}{10}$, and then write it as the decimal 0.4. Since decimals numbers are fractions, you can use what you know about multiplying fractions to help you think about how to multiply decimals.

The grid on the left is a tenths grid with one strip shaded. This strip represents $\frac{1}{10}$, or 0.1. On the right, the strip representing 0.1 is shown divided into 10 squares, with one of the squares shaded darkly. This single square is $\frac{1}{10}$ of $\frac{1}{10}$, or 0.1×0.1.

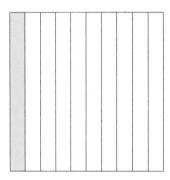
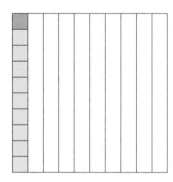

Below the horizontal lines have been extended to make a hundredths grid. This shows that $\frac{1}{10}$ of $\frac{1}{10}$ is one square out of a hundred squares, which is $\frac{1}{100}$, or 0.01 of the whole.

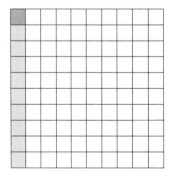

When you multiply 0.1 by 0.1 on your calculator, you get 0.01. What is the fraction name for 0.01? It is $\frac{1}{100}$, as you saw with the grid model.

In the next problem, you explore what happens when you multiply decimals on your calculator. Before you use a calculator to find an exact answer, think about how big you expect the answer to be.

Problem 6.3

A. Look at each set of multiplication problems below. Estimate how large you expect the answer to each problem to be. Will the answer be larger or smaller than 1? Will it be larger or smaller than $\frac{1}{2}$?

Set 1	Set 2	Set 3	Set 4
$21 \times 1 =$	$2.1 \times 1 =$	$0.21 \times 1 =$	$2.1 \times 11 =$
$21 \times 0.1 =$	$2.1 \times 0.1 =$	$0.21 \times 0.1 =$	$2.1 \times 1.1 =$
$21 \times 0.01 =$	$2.1 \times 0.01 =$	$0.21 \times 0.01 =$	$2.1 \times 0.11 =$
$21 \times 0.001 =$	$2.1 \times 0.001 =$	$0.21 \times 0.001 =$	$2.1 \times 0.011 =$
$21 \times 0.0001 =$	$2.1 \times 0.0001 =$	$0.21 \times 0.0001 =$	$2.1 \times 0.0011 =$

B. Use your calculator to do the multiplication, and record the answers in an organized way so that you can look for patterns. Describe any patterns that you see.

C. In a multiplication problem, there is a relationship between the number of decimal places in the factors and the number of decimal places in the product. Summarize what you think this relationship is. Show your reasoning.

Problem 6.3 Follow-Up

1. Test the relationship you discovered in part C on these two problems:

$0.5 \times 4 =$ $5 \times 0.4 =$

Now do the two problems on your calculator. What does the calculator show? Why?

2. When you multiply a number by 10, do you get a larger number or a smaller number? Why? Give three examples to support your answer.

3. When you multiply a number by 0.1, do you get a larger number or a smaller number? Why? Give three examples to support your answer.

6.4 Shifting Decimal Points

Now that you have seen how the positions of decimal points affect products, you can use these ideas to build a deeper understanding of multiplication. In this problem, you will work backward to find numbers with products that fit certain constraints.

Problem 6.4

A. 1. Find two numbers with a product of 1344.
2. Find two numbers with a product of 134.4.
3. Find two numbers with a product of 1.344.
4. Find two numbers with a product of 0.1344.
5. Explain how you got your answers and why you think they are correct.

B. 1. Find two numbers with a product between 2000 and 3000.
2. By moving decimal points, change the value of each of the numbers you found in part 1 so that their product is between 200 and 300.
3. By moving decimal points, change the value of each of the numbers you found in part 1 so that their product is between 20 and 30.
4. By moving decimal points, change the value of each of the numbers you found in part 1 so that their product is between 2 and 3.
5. Explain what you did to get your answers and why you think they are correct.

■ Problem 6.4 Follow-Up

1. What number times 6 gives the product 0.36? Explain.
2. What number times 0.9 gives the product 2.7? Explain.
3. What number times 1.5 gives the product 0.045? Explain.
4. What number times 0.12 gives the product 24? Explain.

6.5 Fencing a Yard

Kelly has a new Golden Retriever. The dog is full of energy and needs some safe space in which to exercise. Kelly has several friends who have agreed to help her fence in part of her yard—she just needs to buy the materials for the fence.

Problem 6.5

Kelly wants to fence in a rectangular space in her yard, 9 meters by 7.5 meters. The salesperson at the supply store recommends that she put up posts every $1\frac{1}{2}$ meters. The posts cost $2.19 each. Kelly will also need to buy wire mesh to string between the posts. The wire mesh is sold by the meter from large rolls and costs $5.98 a meter. A gate to fit in one of the spaces between the posts costs $25.89. Seven staples are needed to attach the wire mesh to each post. Staples come in boxes of 50, and each box costs $3.99.

A. How much will the materials Kelly needs cost before sales tax? Show how you arrived at your answer.

B. Local sales tax is 7%. How much will Kelly's total bill be?

■ Problem 6.5 Follow-Up

Using centimeter grid paper, draw a diagram of the fence. Draw the diagram carefully and accurately, and mark the position of each post and the gate.

As you work on these ACE questions, use your calculator whenever you need it.

Applications

In 1–3, estimate the answer, and explain how you made your estimate.

1. $23.54 + $7.98 + $3.45 + $13.03 ≈

2. $119.56 − $22.90 ≈

3. $15.10 × 12 ≈

4. Mr. Sandival's class is growing a plant. Each of the five teams in his class measured the height of the plant at the end of the first week and at the end of the second week. Here is a table of their measurements.

	Team 1	Team 2	Team 3	Team 4	Team 5
First week	3.4 cm	3.25 cm	3.3 cm	3.5 cm	3.35 cm
Second week	7.95 cm	7.8 cm	8 cm	8.15 cm	8.2 cm

   a. All the teams measured the same plant. Why are the measures different?

   b. Find the mean of the teams' measures for each week.

   c. Using the means, how much did the plant grow from the first week to the second week?

5. Samuel buys the following at the grocery store:

   two dozen eggs at $0.75 a dozen

   one pound of butter at $1.39

   a 5-pound bag of sugar for $1.79

   two 5-pound bags of flour at $1.19 each

   an 8-ounce package of unsweetened chocolate for $1.64

   If Samuel pays 3% sales tax, how much is his bill?

6. Loren is laying decorative brick along both edges of the 21-meter walkway up to his house. Each brick is 0.26 meters long. He is placing the bricks end to end. How many bricks does he need to do the job?

7. Lynette has a beautiful box that she wants to protect. She has been advised to put a strip of molding along each edge of the box to protect it. She measures the edges and finds that the length is 0.75 meters, the width is 0.4 meters, and the height is 0.22 meters.

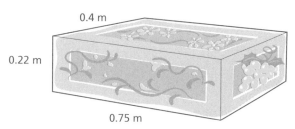

0.4 m

0.22 m

0.75 m

a. Lynette decides she needs four of each of these lengths. Is she correct? Explain.

b. How much molding does Lynette need in all?

c. If the molding costs $0.90 a meter, how much will Lynette's bill be without sales tax?

d. If the sales tax is 4%, how much will her final bill be?

Connections

8. What happens to a decimal number when you multiply it by 10 repeatedly? Use an example to explain your thinking.

9. What happens to a decimal number when you multiply it by 5 repeatedly? Use an example to explain your thinking.

10. Use your calculator to explore what happens to a decimal number when you divide it by 10 repeatedly. Use an example to explain your thinking.

11. In a–d, each mark on the number line is spaced so that the distance between two consecutive marks is the same. Copy each number line and label the marks.

a.

b.

c.

d.

e. Explain how you figured out what the labels should be.

Extensions

12. The table on the next page lists the winners of the gold medal in nine consecutive Olympic meets in men's springboard diving. The points are awarded for the difficulty and the execution of the dive.

In a–c, give evidence to support your conclusion. You may want to make a table of the differences between each pair of years.

a. Between what two years did the greatest change in winning score occur?

b. Between what two years did the next greatest change in winning score occur?

c. Between what two years did the least change in winning score occur?

d. What is the average of Greg Louganis's scores?

Men's Springboard Diving

Year	Winner (country)	Score
1960	Gary Tobian (USA)	170
1964	Kenneth Stizberger (USA)	150.9
1968	Bernie Wrightson (USA)	170.15
1972	Vladimir Vasin (USSR)	594.09
1976	Phil Boggs (USA)	619.52
1980	Aleksandr Portnov (USSR)	905.02
1984	Greg Louganis (USA)	754.41
1988	Greg Louganis (USA)	730.8
1992	Mark Lenzi (USA)	676.53

13   **a.** Show four *different* ways to fill in the missing numbers on the number line.

2.1

  b. Add the five numbers in each of your answers in part a. Do you see a pattern?

  c. Can you find four numbers for the blanks on this number line so that the sum of the five numbers will be 10? Why or why not?

2.1

Mathematical Reflections

In this investigation, you explored adding, subtracting, and multiplying decimals. You looked for relationships between whole-number and decimal computation. These questions will help you summarize what you have learned:

1 Describe in words, and illustrate with one or more examples, how to add two decimal numbers without using a calculator. Explain why your method makes sense.

2 Test your method from part 1 on this sum: 23.0574 + 11.99. Does your method tell you how to handle this case? If not, adjust your description so that someone reading it would know how to add these two decimals.

3 Describe in words, and illustrate with one or more examples, how you subtract two decimal numbers without using a calculator. Explain why your method makes sense.

4 Test your method from part 3 on this difference: 23.05 − 11.9863. Does your method tell you how to handle this case? If not, adjust your description so that someone reading it would know how to subtract these two decimals.

5 How is the number of decimal places in the product of two decimal numbers related to the number of decimal places in each of the numbers? Why is this so?

6 a. Find or create an example in which the product of two decimals is smaller than either of the numbers that are multiplied.

b. Find or create an example in which the product of two decimals is smaller than one of the numbers multiplied but larger than the other.

c. Find or create an example in which the product of two decimals is larger than either of the numbers multiplied.

d. Look for patterns that will help you predict which of these results—a, b, or c—will be the case with any multiplication problem that you do.

Think about these questions, discuss your ideas with other students and your teacher, and then write a summary of your findings in your journal.